Letterland

16 pages

Early Years Workbook 3

Letters: n-s

Name:

Nn

Find Noisy Nick's letters in the nut tree. Make them green.

Write Noisy Nick's letter here.

Find the four things in Noisy Nick's net that begin with his sound. Colour them.

Nn

Can you draw something that makes a lot of noise?

Find Oscar Orange's letters in the orange box. Make them orange.

Write Oscar Orange's letter here.

Say what each picture is. Circle the ones that begin with Oscar Orange's sound.

Now draw an octopus on top of the box.

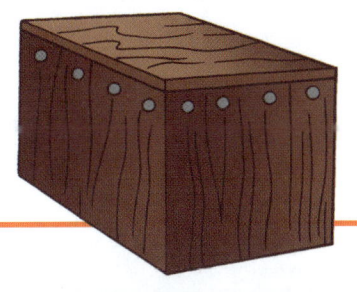

Colour the oranges that are on the table. How many are on the floor?

There are ☐ oranges on the floor.

Mr O, the Old Man from over the ocean, says his name in words. Join Mr O to the things that begin with his sound.

open door

old man

oak tree

octopus

Find Peter Puppy's letters in the park. Make them pink or purple.

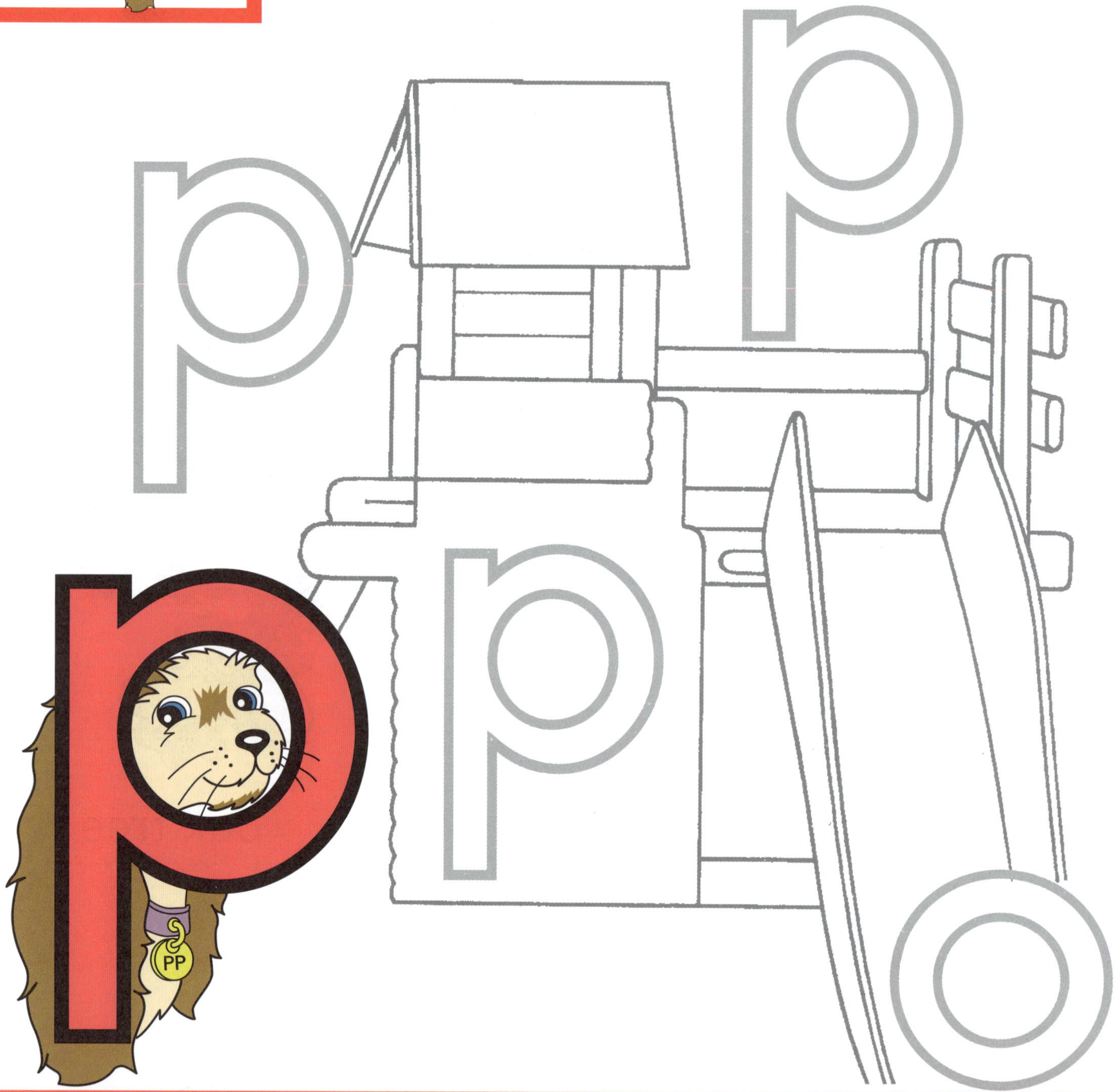

Write Peter Puppy's letter here.

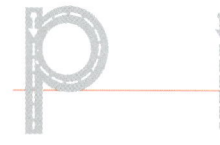

Put a tick (✓) beside the fruits that begin with Peter Puppy's sound. Colour them.

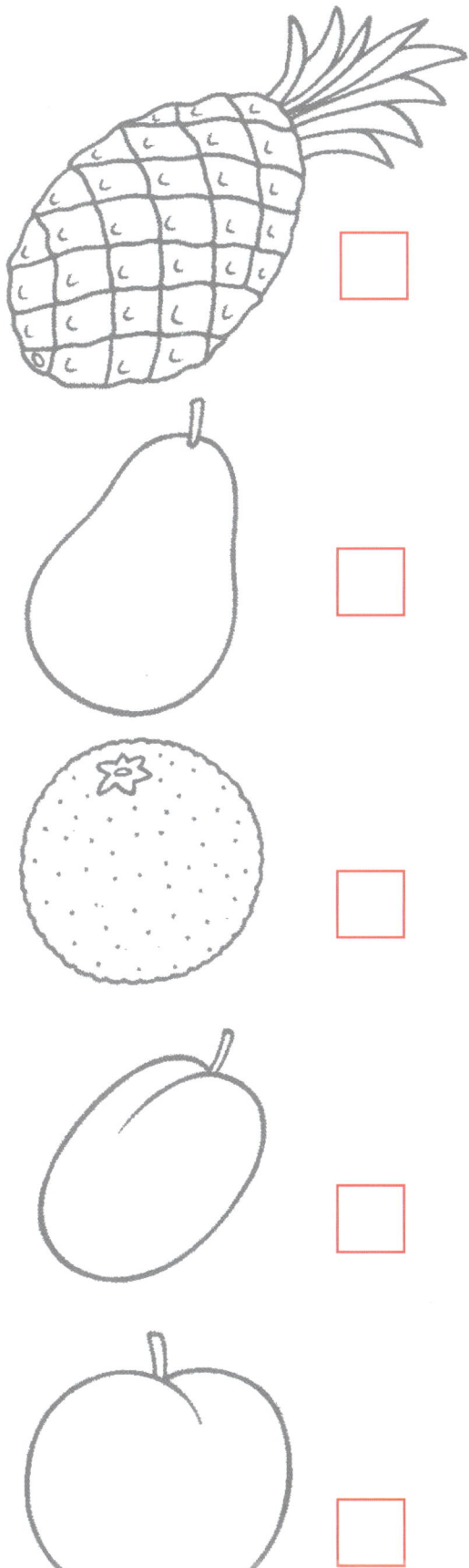

What would you like to eat at a picnic? Draw it.

Find Quarrelsome Queen's letters on her quilt. Make them blue.

Write Quarrelsome Queen's letter here.

Can you quickly colour the pictures that begin with Quarrelsome Queen's sound?

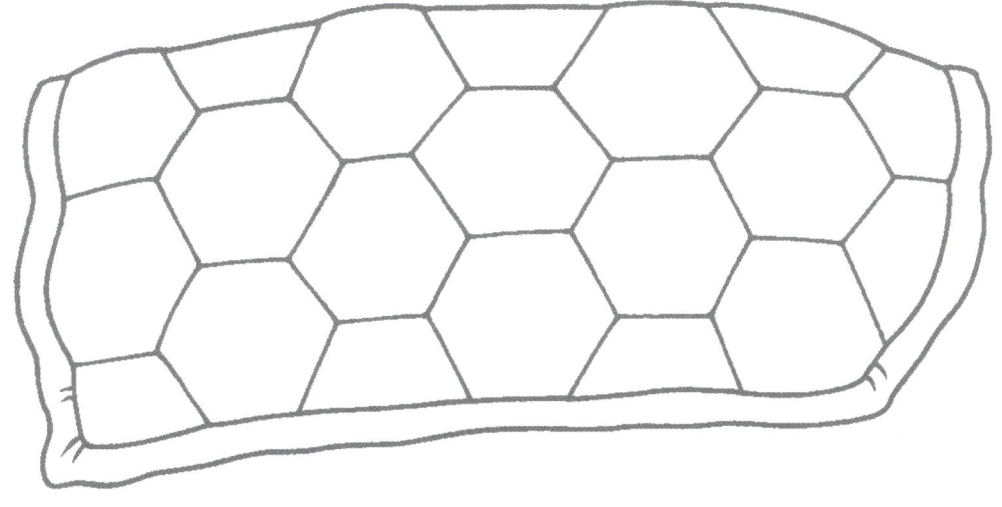

Draw a picture of yourself doing something quiet.

Find Red Robot's letters in the rocket. Make them red.

Write Red Robot's letter here.

Find the things in Red Robot's sack that begin with his sound. Make them red.

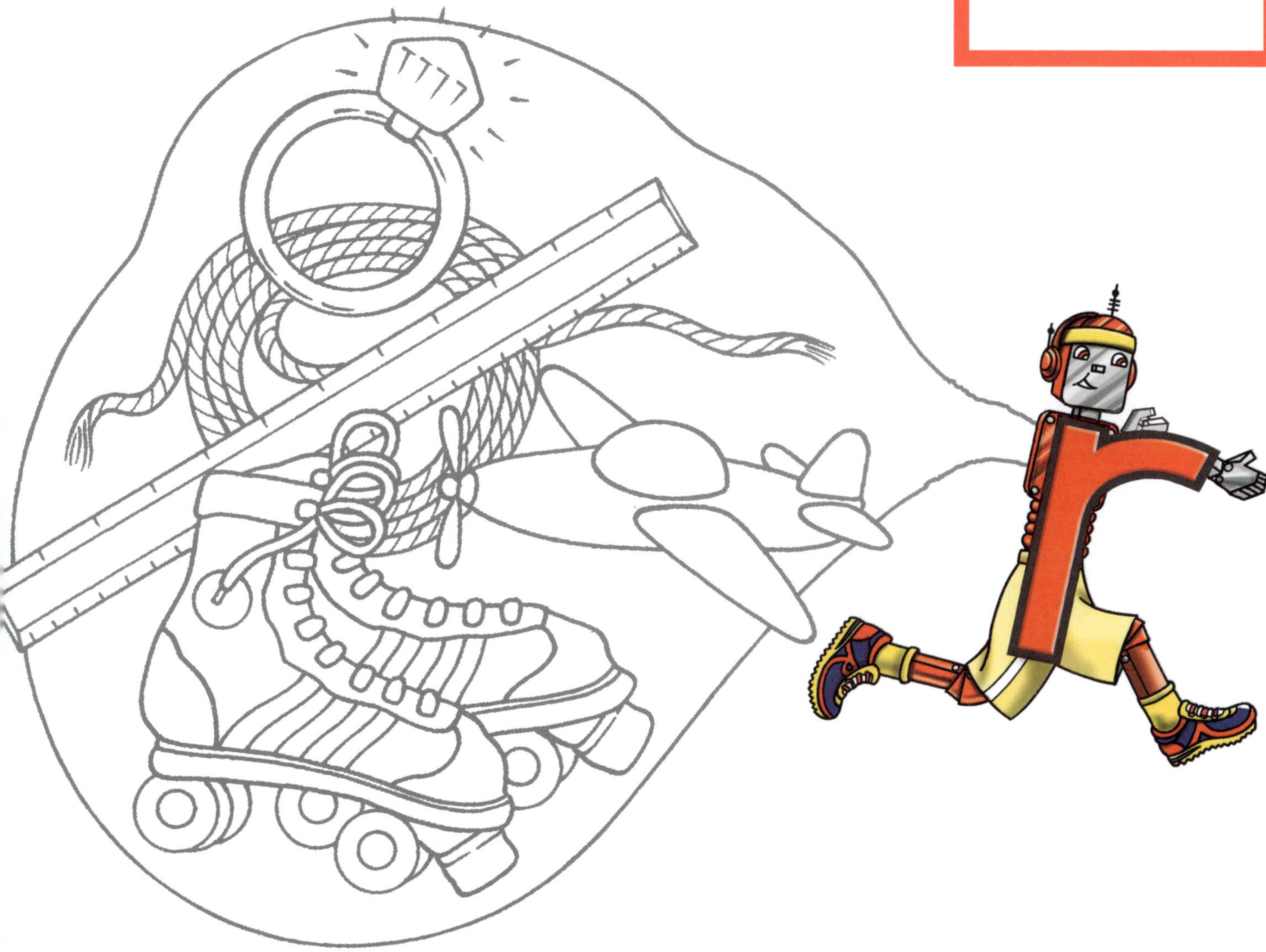

Now draw a picture of your own robot.

Search for Sammy Snake's letters in the sea. Make them yellow.

Write Sammy Snake's letter here.

Help Sammy Snake swim across the sea to the other side. Go over the waves with a pencil. Then slowly say what each picture is.

Look at the names under each picture.
Then draw the Letterlander.

Noisy Nick

Oscar Orange

Peter Puppy

Quarrelsome Queen

Red Robot

Sammy Snake

Published by Letterland International Ltd.
8/10 South Street, Epsom, Surrey, KT18 7PF, UK
© Letterland International 2006
ISBN: 978-1-86209-351-5

First published 1997.
This revised edition published 2006.
Reprinted 2008, 2011, 2012, 2014, 2018, 2020, 2021, 2023.
18 17 16 15 14

LETTERLAND™ is a trademark of Letterland International Ltd.

Written by Louis Fidge
Illustrated by Anna Jupp and Kathy Baxendale
Consultant: Lyn Wendon, originator of Letterland

Code: T61

ISBN 978-1-86209-351-5

9 781862 093515

 Child-friendly phonics

All rights reserved. No part of this publication may be reproduced, stored in a retrieval system, or transmitted in any form or by any means, electronic, mechanical, photocopying, recording or otherwise, without the prior permission of the Publisher or a licence permitting restricted copying in the United Kingdom issued by the Copyright Licensing Agency Ltd, 90 Tottenham Court Road, London W1P 0LP.

British Library Cataloguing in Publication Data. A catalogue record for this book is available from the British Library.

Printed in Guangdong Province, China.